PO PIANO AND KEYBOARDS

ENTRY ZONE ➤ Grade 1

A *Rockschool* Publication
Broomfield House, Broomfield Road, Richmond, Surrey TW9 3HS

Welcome To *Popular Piano* Grade 1

Welcome to the Rockschool *Popular Piano and Electronic Keyboards* Grade 1 pack. This pack contains everything you need to play popular piano in this grade. In the book you will find the exam scores in standard notation with fingering suggestions. The CD features performances of the tunes (with no digital edits) to help you learn the pieces. There are also ten practice ear tests. Handy tips on playing the pieces and the marking schemes can be found in the Guru's Guide on page 15. If you have any queries about this or any other Rockschool exam, please call us on **020 8332 6303** or email us at **office@rockschool.co.uk** or visit our website **http://www.rockschool.co.uk**. Good luck!

Entry Zone Techniques in Debut and Grade 1

The eight Rockschool grades are divided into four Zones. *Popular Piano and Electronic Keyboards* Grade 1, along with Debut, is part of the *Entry Zone*. This Zone is for players who are just starting out and who are looking to build a solid technical and stylistic foundation for their playing.

Debut: in Debut you will be concentrating on playing tunes. A player of Debut standard should be able to play up to 16 bars of music in either 2/2, 3/4 or 4/4 time, using simple melodies composed of semibreves, minims, crotchets and associated rests.

Grade 1: in this grade you should be able to play up to 20 bars of music using melodies composed of semibreves, minims, crotchets, quavers and associated rests.

Popular Piano and Electronic Keyboards Exams at Grade 1

Players wishing to enter for a *Popular Piano and Electronic Keyboards* Grade 1 exam need to prepare **three** pieces, of which **one** may be a free choice piece chosen from outside the printed repertoire. In addition, you must prepare the technical exercises in this book, undertake either a sight reading test or an improvisation & interpretation test, take an ear test and answer general musicianship questions. Samples of these are printed in the books.

Instrument specification and performances in the exam

Candidates bringing in their own instrument must ensure that their keyboard is suitable for the technical requirements of the grade. Electronic keyboards should conform to the following specification: 5 octave keyboard (touch sensitive), keyboard stand, amplification (if required), sustain pedal and all relevant audio and power leads. Keyboards should have a 'realistic' acoustic piano sound which must be used for performance in the exam.

Music Notation Explained

THE MUSICAL STAVE shows pitches and rhythms and is divided by lines into bars. Pitches are named after the first seven letters of the alphabet.

Definitions For Special Piano Notation

Grace Note: Play the grace note on or before the beat depending on the style of music, then move quickly to the note it leads onto.

Spread Chord: Play the chord from the bottom note up, with the top note being reached by the appropriate notated bar position.

Tremolando: Oscillate at speed between marked notes.

Pedal Marking: Depress and then release the sustain pedal.

Glissando: Play the notes before the beat as smoothly as possible.

Finger Markings: These numbers represent your fingers. 1 is the thumb, 2 the index finger and so on.

 (accent) • Accentuate note (play it louder).

 (accent) • Accentuate note with great intensity.

 (staccato) • Shorten time value of note.

 (accent) • Accentuate note with more arm weight.

D.%. al Coda • Go back to the sign (%), then play until the bar marked *To Coda* ✛ then skip to the section marked ✛ *Coda*.

D.C. al Fine • Go back to the beginning of the song and play until the bar marked *Fine* (end).

Una Corda • Use damper (soft) pedal

 • Repeat bars between signs.

 • When a repeated section has different endings, play the first ending only the first time and the second ending only the second time.

Choo Choo Train Boogie

Adrian York

Ten-to-Ten

Tim Richards

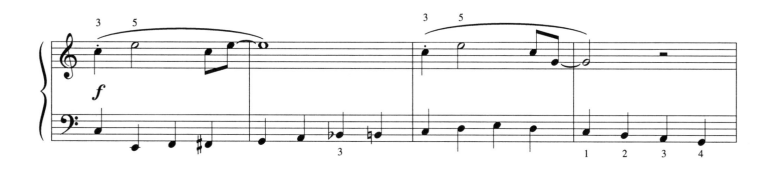

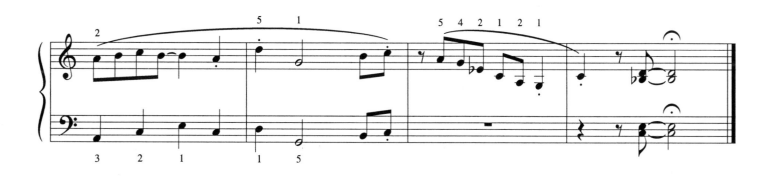

In The Red Feeling Blue

Simon Wallace

Just One More Chance

Terry Seabrook

Ariapeta Avenue

Mark Cherrie

Cat & Mouse

Janette Mason

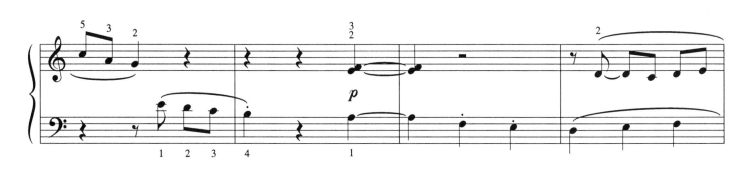

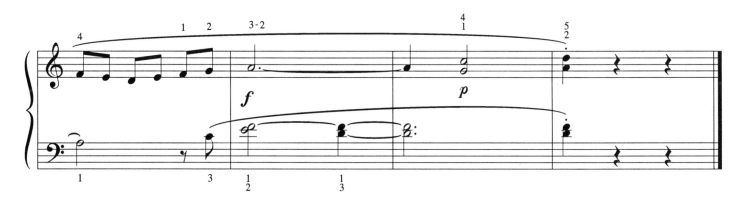

Technical Exercises

In this section, the examiner will ask you to play a selection of exercises drawn from each of the two groups shown below. These exercises contain examples of the kinds of scales and arpeggios you can use when playing the pieces. You do not need to memorise the exercises (and can use the book in the exam) but the examiner will be looking for the speed of your response. The examiner will also give credit for the level of your musicality. All exercises should be prepared hands separately ascending and descending in the keys and octaves specified. The fingerings shown below are suggestions only.

The exercises should be played ascending and descending as shown at ♩=60 with a straight feel.

Group A: Scales

C Major Scale - Right Hand

C Major Scale - Left Hand

A Aeolian Scale - Right Hand

A Aeolian Scale - Left Hand

C Major Pentatonic - Right Hand (3 Note Pattern)

C Major Pentatonic - Left Hand (3 Note Pattern)

E Minor Pentatonic - Right Hand (3 Note Pattern)

E Minor Pentatonic - Left Hand (3 Note Pattern)

Group B: Broken Chords

G Major Broken Chord - Right Hand

G Major Broken Chord - Left Hand

A Minor Broken Chord - Right Hand

A Minor Broken Chord - Left Hand

Sight Reading *or* Improvisation & Interpretation

In this section you have a choice between either a sight reading test or an improvisation & interpretation test. Printed below is an example of the type of **sight reading** test you are likely to excounter in the exam. The piece will be composed in the style of one of the six performance pieces. The examiner will allow you 90 seconds to prepare it and will set the tempo for you on a metronome.

Printed below is an example of the type of **improvisation & interpretation** test you are likely to encounter in an exam. You will be asked to play an improvised part based on a chord chart in the style of one of the six performance pieces. The examiner will allow you 90 seconds to prepare it and will set the tempo for you on a metronome.

Ear Tests

You will find two ear tests in this grade. The examiner will play each test to you twice on CD. You will find ten examples of the type of test you will get in the exam printed below.

Test 1 (CD Tracks 7 to 11)

You will be asked to play back on your piano/electronic keyboard a simple melody consisting of the first three notes of the G major scale (G, A and B above middle C), crotchets only. You will be given the key and the first note by the examiner and you will hear the sequence twice.

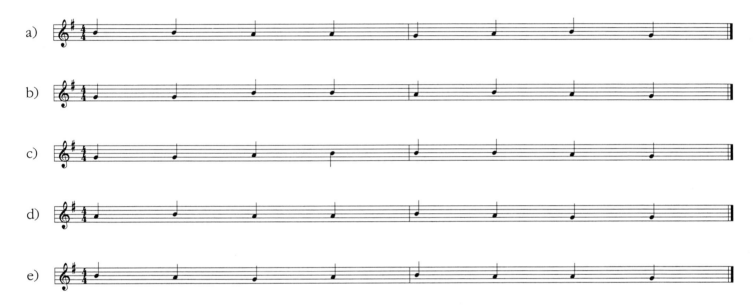

Test 2 (CD Tracks 12 to 16)

You will be asked to clap back the rhythm of a simple two bar melody after hearing it twice.

General Musicianship Questions

You will be asked five General Musicianship Questions at the end of the exam.

Topics:

i)   Music theory
ii) Knowledge of your instrument

The music theory questions will cover the following topics at this grade:

Recognition of pitches   Dynamic Markings (*p*, *mf* and *f*)
Note Values   Rests
Time Signatures   Key Signatures
Fermata (Pause)

Knowledge of the construction of the following chord types in the keys of the pieces played by you in the exam. Tonic (chord I) only.

Major   (Root position)
Minor   (Root position)

The instrument knowledge questions will cover the following topics at this grade:

Plugging into the amplifier and keyboard (electronic keyboard only)
Correct unplugging procedure (electronic keyboard only)
Volume and tone adjustments on the keyboard (electronic keyboard only)
Appropriate choice of sound (electronic keyboard only)

Knowledge of parts of the piano/electronic keyboard:

Keyboard, black and white keys, sustain and damping pedals, volume and tone controls as applicable.

Questions on all these topics will be based on pieces played by you in the exam

The Guru's Guide To *Popular Piano* Grade 1

This section contains some handy hints compiled by Rockschool's Popular Piano and Keyboards Guru to help you get the most out of the performance pieces. Do feel free to adapt the tunes to suit your playing style. Remember, these tunes are your chance to show your musical imagination and personality.

Fingerings are suggestions only, so use whichever suit your hands best. Please also note that in tunes with optional solo sections, if the solo option is not taken you should move straight onto the next section.

Popular Piano and Electronic Keyboards Grade 1 Tunes

Rockschool tunes help you play in all the popular piano/keyboard styles you enjoy. The pieces have been written or arranged by top performers and composers according to style specifications drawn up by Rockschool.

Each tune printed here falls into one of six categories: blues, jazz, classic, pop/rock, world and film music. These cover roots, contemporary and global styles that influence every generation of performers.

CD track 1   *Blues*   ***Choo Choo Train Boogie***

A classic 'train' boogie in the tradition of Meade Lux Lewis's *Honky Tonk Train Blues* that needs to be played with an authentic boogie feel. Imagine that the first few bars are an old steam train gradually picking up speed. Watch out for the staccatos and keep the left hand 'rocks' part nice and steady.

Composer: Adrian York. Adrian is Rockschool's piano syllabus director. He is a successful media composer and a fixture on both the jazz and session circuit who has backed many top artists. Rumour has it that a long time ago he used to play in a well known boy band.

CD track 2   *Jazz*   ***Ten-to-Ten***

The action is mainly in the left hand here. Practice it until you are comfortable with the fingering. This style of left hand imitates the walking bass lines used by jazz double bass players although the title refers to the typical swing pattern played by drummers on the ride cymbal. Watch out for the tied notes, dynamics and staccato releases.

Composer: Tim Richards. Tim Richards first encountered a piano at the age of eight in a dentist's waiting room. Since then he has become an acclaimed jazz and blues pianist, band leader, composer and educator. His groups include Spirit Level, The Tim Richards Trio and Great Spirit. He performs with blues artists including Otis Grand and Dana Gillespie. He is also known for his widely respected book *Improvising Blues Piano* (Schott & Co).

CD track 3   *Classic*   ***In The Red Feeling Blue***

This is a tune that requires great finesse and attention to the detail of dynamics, phrasing and articulation. You may find the syncopated rhythms tricky so practice them and don't rush the off beat. Try to capture the feel of world weary sophisticated melancholia that this tune conjures up.

Composer: Simon Wallace. Simon is one of London's top jazz piano players and has written music for nearly every comedy show on British television including *Absolutely Fabulous* and *French and Saunders*.

CD track 4   *Pop/Rock*   ***Just One More Chance***

This piece, influenced by pop stylists such as Carole King and Elton John, needs to be played with a very regular sense of the beat. Try counting 1 & 2 & 3 & 4 & and see how every note sits in one of those slots. If you keep the tempo steady you stand a good chance of pulling off a good performance.

Composer: Terry Seabrook. Terry writes music regularly for television, animated films and adverts. He records and performs with his own Latin group Cubana Bop on the international Jazz and Latin circuit. He also tutors piano as part of the world famous Jamey Aebersold Summer School each year.

CD track 5   *World*   ***Ariapeta Avenue***

A slice of Trinidadian carnival time. Syncopation is the key, especially with bars 3, 4, 6 and 8 where the right hand anticipates the left. Bring each hand together slowly, counting all the time. Watch out for the rhythm of the last bar: 1 2 3 4 5 6 7 8. Take care over note releases and the contrast between legato and staccato.

Composer: Mark Cherrie. Mark started playing Caribbean music professionally at the age of 14 in his fathers band. Since then he and his music have toured the world and he has composed music for many television advertisements and for shows such as *Friends* and *E.R.*

CD track 6   *Film*   ***Cat & Mouse***

This tremulous tribute to cartoon music is a terrific introduction to the dorian mode. The emphasis should be on phrasing, articulation and dynamics. Take care over the right hand fingering three bars from the end.

Composer: Janette Mason. Janette is a top session musician and media composer performing on piano, keyboard and organ with artists as varied as Oasis, Seal, Suzanne Vega, kd lang and Mica Paris. As a composer she has written for advertising campaigns and many Channel Four documentaries.

CD Pianist: David Rees-Williams. David has a dual career as a performer and educator. He teaches at Canterbury Christchurch University College and he works internationally as a performer at concerts and festivals, playing everything from baroque harpsichord to jazz piano.

Grade Exam Marking Scheme

The table below shows the marking scheme for the *Popular Piano and Electronic Keyboards* Grade 1 exam.

ELEMENT	PASS	MERIT	DISTINCTION
Piece 1 Piece 2 Piece 3	13 out of 20 13 out of 20 13 out of 20	15 out of 20 15 out of 20 15 out of 20	17+ out of 20 17+ out of 20 17+ out of 20
Technical Exercises	11 out of 15	12 out of 15	13+ out of 15
Either: Sight Reading *Or:* Improvisation & Interpretation	6 out of 10	7 out of 10	8+ out of 10
Ear Tests	6 out of 10	7 out of 10	8+ out of 10
General Musicianship Questions	3 out of 5	4 out of 5	5 out of 5
Total Marks	**Pass: 65% +**	**Pass: 75% +**	**Pass: 85% +**

Free Choice Song Criteria

You can bring in your own performance pieces to play in any of the exams featured. In the Grade Exams you can bring in **one** piece.

- Players may bring in either their own compositions or songs already in the public domain, including hits from the charts.
- Songs must be performed solo.
- Players should bring in two copies of the piece to be performed, notated either in standard notation, or chord charts. Players must use an original copy of the tune to be performed, and must provide a second copy for the examiner, which may be a photocopy. For copyright reasons, photocopies handed to the examiner will be retained and destroyed by Rockschool in due course.
- Players may perform either complete songs or extracts.
- Players should aim to keep their free choice songs below 3 minutes in length.
- Players should aim to make each free choice song of a technical standard similar to those published in the Rockschool *Popular Piano and Electronic Keyboards* Grade 1 book. However, examiners will be awarding credit for how well you perform the song. In general players should aim to play songs that mix the following physical and expressive techniques and rhythm skills:

Physical Techniques: accurate left and right hand co-ordination, ability to play chords in one hand and melody in the other, simple walking bass patterns and the ability to move from one hand position to another (both hands).

Expressive Techniques: legato, staccato and dynamics.

Rhythm Skills: songs should contain a mixture of semibreves, minims, crotchets and quavers.

You, or your teacher, may wish to adapt an existing piece of music to suit the criteria above. You should ensure that any changes to the music are clearly marked on the sheet submitted to the examiner.

Entering Rockschool Exams

Entering a Rockschool exam is easy. Please read through these instructions carefully before filling in the exam entry form. Information on current exam fees can be obtained from Rock School by ringing **020 8332 6303**

- You should enter for the exam of your choice when you feel ready.

- You can enter for any one of three examination periods. These are shown below with their closing dates.

PERIOD	DURATION	CLOSING DATE
Period A	1st February to 15th March	1st December
Period B	15th May to 31st July	1st April
Period C	1st November to 15th December	1st October

These dates will apply from 1st January 2001 until further notice

- Please fill in the form giving your name, address and phone number. Please tick the type and level of exam, along with the period and year. Finally, fill in the fee box with the appropriate amount. You should send this form with a cheque or postal order to: **Rockschool, Broomfield House, 10 Broomfield Road, Richmond, Surrey TW9 3HS.**

- Rockschool will allocate your entry to a centre closest to your postcode and you will receive notification of the exam, showing a date, location and time as well as advice of what to bring to the centre.

- You should inform Rockschool of any cancellations or alterations to the schedule as soon as you can as it is not possible to transfer entries from one centre, or one period, to another without the payment of an administration fee.

- Please bring your music book to the exam. You may not use photocopied music, nor the music used by someone else in another exam. The examiner will stamp each book after each session. Performers may be barred from taking an exam if they use music not otherwise belonging to them.

- You should aim to arrive for your *Popular Piano and Electronic Keyboards* Grade 1 exam fifteen minutes before the time stated on the schedule.

- The exam centre will have a waiting area which you may use prior to being called into the main exam room.

- Each *Popular Piano and Electronic Keyboards* Grade 1 exam is scheduled to last for 20 minutes. You can use a small proportion of this time to get ready.

- About 2 to 3 weeks after the exam you will receive a typed copy of the examiner's mark sheet. Every successful player will receive a Rockschool certificate of achievement.

- Rockschool may defer your entry to the next available exam period if the minimum number of candidates for your local centre is not met.

- For all up to date information refer to the Rockschool website **http://www.rockschool.co.uk**.